The Open University

Mathematics and Computing/Technology

A Third-level Course

MT365 Graphs, Networks and Design

CONCLUSION

Prepared by the Course Team

Study guide

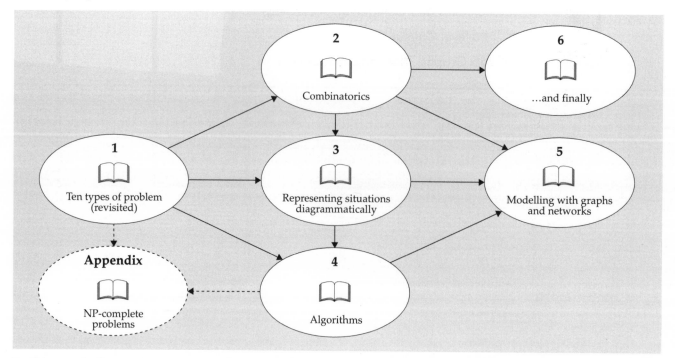

In this concluding unit, we aim to draw together some of the main ideas underlying the course, and also to indicate some new ideas which may be of interest if you wish to continue your study of combinatorics and modelling.

This is a reading unit — there are no problems or exercises. It is designed to survey some of the main themes of the course, with the benefit of hindsight, and to make explicit some common ideas that run through the units. You may find that it helps with your revision — or you may prefer to read it once the examination is over.

In Section 1 we revisit the ten types of problem introduced in the *Introduction* unit and relate them to the rest of the course.

In Sections 2, 3, 4 and 5 we review the main themes of the course — combinatorics, algorithms and mathematical modelling. In particular, we link the subject areas *graphs*, *networks* and *design*. We define a generalization of the concept of a *graph*, called a *hypergraph*, give some examples of hypergraphs which you have already met, and list some unsolved problems. We return to the subject of NP-completeness, and classify some of the algorithms introduced in the course. Finally, in an Appendix, we list some problems which are known to be NP-complete, and some whose status is still unknown.

The Open University, Walton Hall, Milton Keynes, MK7 6AA.

First published 1996. Reprinted 1998, 2002, 2003 , 2005.

Copyright © 1996 The Open University.

Designed by the Graphic Design Group of the Open University.

Typeset in the United Kingdom by the Open University.

Printed in Malta by Gutenberg Press Limited.

ISBN 0 7492 2215 8

This text forms part of an Open University third-level course. If you would like a copy of *Studying with the Open University*, please write to the Central Enquiry Service, PO Box 200, The Open University, Walton Hall, Milton Keynes, MK7 6YZ. If you have not enrolled on the course and would like to buy this or other Open University material, please write to Open University, Educational Enterprises Ltd, 12 Cofferidge Close, Stony Stratford, Milton Keynes, MK11 1BY, United Kingdom.

MT365Conclusion1.4

Contents

Introduction

In this unit, we look back and we look forward. We review many of the ideas and problems encountered in the course, show how they can be generalized and extended, and discuss the progress made in finding solutions.

In the *Introduction* unit, you met a number of problems which you were invited to try to solve. Some of these were straightforward, and were included in order to give you an idea of some of the topics covered in the course. Others were more difficult and illustrated the need for a more systematic approach, given later in the course.

We start, in Section 1, *Ten types of problem (revisited)*, by returning to the ten problems with which we started the course, and relating them to the rest of the course.

In Section 2, *Combinatorics*, we return to the main themes of the course and review the four types of combinatorial problem: existence, construction, enumeration and optimization problems. We also classify several of the problems encountered in the course.

In Section 3, *Representing situations diagrammatically*, we show how some of the problems introduced throughout the course can be modelled by means of graphs and networks or by using the concept of a *hypergraph*.

In Section 4, *Algorithms*, we return to the topic of NP-completeness. We discuss the efficiency of the algorithms we have introduced throughout the course, and show where many of the graph algorithms fit into the hierarchy given in *Graphs 4*.

In Section 5, *Modelling with graphs and networks*, we make some general remarks about graph and network models. We conclude, in Section 6, *... and finally*, with a few general strategies that you may find useful when tackling combinatorial questions.

1   Ten types of problem (revisited)

In this section, we return to the ten types of problem that you met at the beginning of the course. Most of the instances of problems mentioned there were necessarily expressed in rather simple form, since at that stage we had no appropriate technical language to describe the problems and no suitable techniques with which to solve them. All of them were instances of more substantial problems that you studied later.

We now review our progress in tackling these ten types of problem, and we relate them to other topics in the course.

1.1   Map colouring

Consider the following map of the United States of America (excluding Alaska and Hawaii).

We posed the following questions:

> how many colours are needed to colour the entire map, when neighbouring states are coloured differently?

> how many colours are needed to colour any map?

In *Graphs 3* we answered the related existence problem:

> does there exist a map that cannot be coloured with four colours?

We saw that the answer to this last question is NO. In 1976 K. Appel and W. Haken proved that all maps can be coloured with just four colours; their proof was very complicated, and involved the use of many hours of computer time. Thus this problem has been answered completely, provided that we accept this type of 'proof'.

In *Graphs 3* we represented a map by a graph and re-stated the map colouring problem as a vertex colouring problem:

> can every planar graph be vertex coloured with four colours so that adjacent vertices are coloured differently?

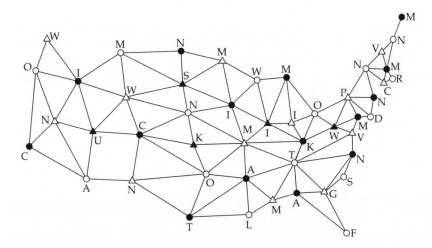

We saw that a 4-colouring of such a graph splits the set of vertices into four disjoint subsets, corresponding to the four colours. Such a vertex decomposition has the property that no two vertices in the same set are adjacent.

We also saw instances of other problems related to these, such as those involving colouring the *edges* of a graph. There are no known efficient algorithms for vertex colouring or for edge colouring, although there are various theorems that give upper and lower bounds on the chromatic number $\chi(G)$ and the chromatic index $\chi'(G)$.

1.2 Tilings

If we attempt to tile a flat surface with tiles, we find that only certain shapes and arrangements are possible. Given a supply of tiles of assorted shapes, we cannot guarantee that they will all fit neatly together without gaps or overlaps. However, if all the tiles are regular polygons of the same size and shape, then we can determine whether such a tiling is possible; such a tiling is called a **regular tiling.**

In *Graphs 1*, we saw that we can tile the plane with congruent *equilateral triangles*, *squares*, or regular *hexagons*, but not with any other congruent regular polygons.

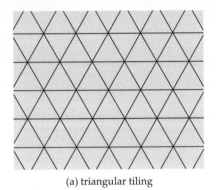

(a) triangular tiling

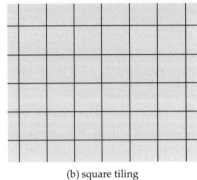

(b) square tiling

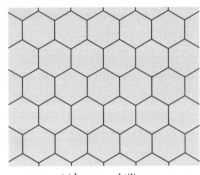

(c) hexagonal tiling

We next tried to construct tilings from regular polygons of two or more different types, where the arrangement of the polygons at each vertex is the same; such a tiling is called a **semi-regular tiling**.

In *Design 1, Geometry* we investigated which semi-regular tilings were possible, and we presented a complete list of them.

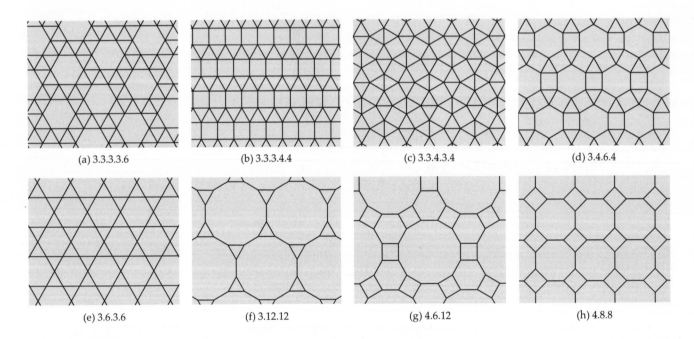

(a) 3.3.3.3.6   (b) 3.3.3.4.4   (c) 3.3.4.3.4   (d) 3.4.6.4

(e) 3.6.3.6   (f) 3.12.12   (g) 4.6.12   (h) 4.8.8

We also saw that there are infinitely many **demi-regular tilings** — tilings by regular polygons with more than one vertex type.

However, suppose that we are given a supply of polygonal tiles that are not necessarily regular or convex, and asked to determine whether they tile the plane. Such problems often turn out to be very difficult, and little is known about their solutions in general.

We return to this topic in Section 4.

1.3 Connection problems

The diagram in the margin represents a telecommunication network. The points labelled *A–J* represent telephone exchanges, and the lines represent links connecting them in pairs. Such a telecommunication network is vulnerable in two ways: for example, telephone lines and cables may be damaged by natural causes and closed for repairs, and exchanges may be put out of action by malfunctioning equipment, repairs or earthquakes.

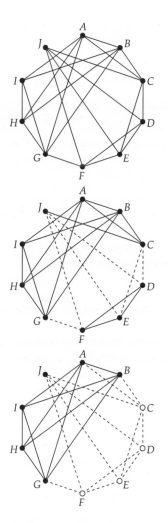

Suppose that, at times, some of the *links* in the above network are out of use; this may make connections (direct or indirect) between some exchanges impossible. We posed the following questions:

> what is the smallest number of links whose closure would separate the network into two parts?

> which are the corresponding links?

At other times, some of the *exchanges* may be out of action, and so the links connected to these exchanges also become useless; this may make connections between some exchanges impossible. We posed the following questions:

> what is the smallest number of exchanges whose closure would separate the network into two parts?

> which are the corresponding exchanges?

In *Networks 1* we rephrased these problems in terms of the *edge connectivity* and *vertex connectivity* of a graph, and we saw that the answers to these questions are closely linked with the number of *vertex-disjoint* or *edge-disjoint* paths between pairs of vertices in the network. These results were summarized in *Menger's theorems*, which are examples of *minimax theorems* — the minimum of some quantity equals the maximum of another.

A related, and more elementary, idea is that of a *connected* graph, introduced in *Graphs 1*. This extremely important idea occurred frequently throughout the course. For example, in *Design 4* we discussed the advantages in experimental design of constructing *connected* designs — those that can be represented by connected graphs.

Another use of connected graphs appears in Section 1.6.

1.4 The Königsberg bridges problem

In the early eighteenth century the mediaeval city of Königsberg contained a central island around which the river flowed before dividing into two. The four parts of the city (*A, B, C* and *D*) were interconnected by seven bridges (*a, b, c, d, e, f* and *g*), as shown in the diagram on the left:

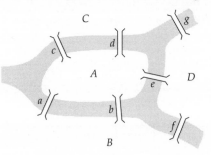
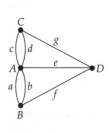

The citizens of Königsberg posed the question:

> does there exist a route that crosses each bridge exactly once, and returns to the starting point? and if so, what is it?

However, they could find no such route. In the *Introduction* unit we modelled the problem using the graph on the right; we found that this was a useful way to solve the problem.

In *Graphs 1*, we defined Eulerian graphs and their vertex analogues, Hamiltonian graphs, as follows.

A connected graph is *Eulerian* if it contains a closed trail that includes every *edge*; such a trail is an *Eulerian trail*.

A connected graph is *Hamiltonian* if it contains a cycle that includes every *vertex*; such a cycle is a *Hamiltonian cycle*.

Euler found a necessary and sufficient condition for a connected graph to be Eulerian (every vertex has even degree), but no such result is known for Hamiltonian graphs.

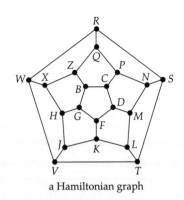

a Hamiltonian graph

We also showed how these concepts can be extended to digraphs, and gave applications to telecommunications (the rotating drum problem) and statistics (ranking in tournaments). In *Networks 2*, we gave matrix methods for finding Eulerian trails and Hamiltonian cycles in digraphs, but we did not comment on their efficiency.

We return to this topic in Section 4.

1.5   Network flows

The following diagram represents a physical network of pipelines along which a fluid flows from a source S to a sink T. Each of the intermediate points A–I represents a pipe junction at which the total inward flow is equal to the total outward flow. Each line between two junctions represents a pipeline of given capacity.

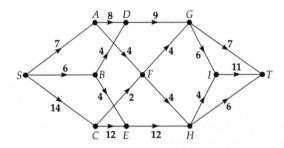

In the *Introduction* unit, we saw how 15 units of flow can be sent from S to T, and we asked

how do we know when we have a maximum flow?

Such problems were discussed in *Networks 1*, where we proved an important minimax theorem called the *max-flow min-cut theorem*:

the value of a maximum flow is equal to the capacity of a minimum cut.

The above network has a minimum cut of capacity 23; thus the value of a maximum flow is 23.

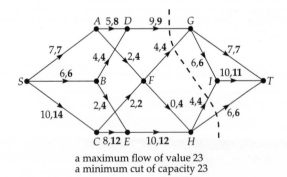

a maximum flow of value 23
a minimum cut of capacity 23

The max-flow min-cut theorem is closely related to the ideas of connectivity and Menger's theorems, mentioned above in Section 1.3.

We also presented the *maximum flow algorithm* for constructing a maximum flow in a basic network. In our examples all the capacities were integers and the networks were simple; we did not consider other cases or address the following questions. Would the algorithm work for a network containing cycles? How fast is it for a network with a large number of arcs? Is it a good algorithm?

We return to this topic in Section 4.

1.6   Braced rectangular frameworks

Many buildings are supported by rectangular steel frameworks, and it is important that such frameworks should remain rigid under heavy loads. One way to achieve this is to add braces, to prevent distortion in the plane. The following diagram shows a simple 3×3 rigid framework with five braces in the form of rectangular plates. As the complexity of the framework increases, it becomes increasingly difficult to visualize the possible distortions and to determine whether the framework is rigid.

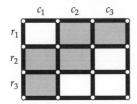   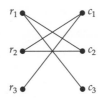

In the *Introduction* unit, we showed how such a problem can be modelled by a graph, and in *Design 2* we showed that a framework is rigid if and only if the associated graph is connected. We also saw that a minimum bracing of the framework corresponds to the case in which the associated graph has as few edges as possible — that is, when it is a *spanning tree*. Thus we can translate all such problems into problems about connected graphs and their spanning trees.

The concept of a spanning tree is fundamental. It plays a role in the minimum connector problem, in the study of tree searches described in *Graphs 4*, and in the theory of electrical networks presented in *Networks 4*.

The idea of a spanning tree was originally introduced by G. R. Kirchhoff in 1847, in a paper on electrical networks.

1.7   Job assignment

A building contractor advertises five jobs — those of bricklayer, carpenter, decorator, electrician and plumber. There are four applicants — one for carpenter and decorator, one for bricklayer, carpenter and plumber, one for decorator, electrician and plumber, and one for carpenter and electrician. Can all the applicants be assigned to jobs for which they are qualified?

applicant	job
1	c,d
2	b,c,p
3	d,e,p
4	c,e

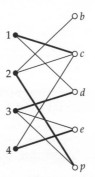

In the *Introduction* unit, we saw that one possible assignment of applicants to jobs is

1-carpenter, 2-plumber, 3-decorator, 4-electrician.

Such problems are called *matching* problems. They can become extremely complicated when there are a large number of applicants and jobs. An assignment of applicants to jobs is a *matching*; an assignment which allocates as many applicants as possible to jobs is a *maximum matching*.

The problem of finding a maximum matching is closely related to that of finding a maximum flow.

In *Networks 3*, we showed how any problem of this type can be represented in terms of finding a matching in a graph, and we presented the *maximum matching algorithm* which can be used to solve it.

Sometimes the applicants have different abilities to do the various jobs, and the abilities are specified by a cost matrix.

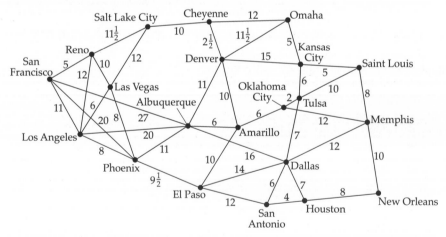

This type of problem is an *assignment* problem, which can be solved by the *Hungarian algorithm*. Both algorithms start with an initial assignment of people to jobs, and then build up solutions systematically.

A related problem is the *transportation* problem, which can be solved using a version of the Hungarian algorithm.

1.8   Optimal routes

The following map gives some possible routes for a traveller wishing to drive from San Francisco to St. Louis; the numbers indicate the driving times (in hours) between pairs of cities. The problem is to find the quickest route between the two cities.

Such route maps quickly become complicated as the number of intermediate cities increases, and thus a systematic method for determining the quickest route is needed. In *Networks 2*, we presented an efficient algorithm, the *shortest path algorithm*, for solving any problem of this type for weighted digraphs. We also presented a related algorithm, the *longest path algorithm*, for weighted digraphs *with no cycles*, but did not discuss the efficiency of these algorithms.

We return to this topic in Section 4.

The idea of finding a longest path is related to another important optimization problem — that of scheduling activities involved in a complicated project by finding a critical path in an activity network.

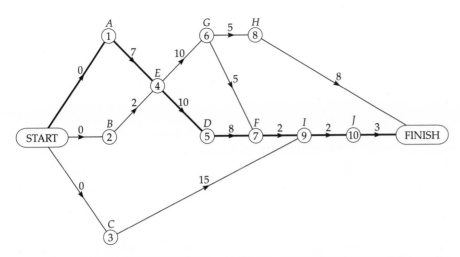

For this problem we presented the *critical path construction algorithm* and a heuristic algorithm for scheduling a project for a given number of workers, called the *critical path scheduling algorithm*; unfortunately, this does not always produce an optimum schedule.

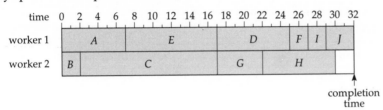

1.9 Minimum connector problems

Consider an electricity company that wants to lay a network of cables to link together five towns, *A, B, C, D* and *E*, and wishes to minimize the total amount of cabling. Such a connecting route of minimum total length is called a *minimum connector*.

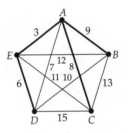

In the *Introduction* unit and in *Graphs 2*, we presented two efficient 'greedy' algorithms, *Kruskal's algorithm* and *Prim's algorithm*, for solving any problem of this type. These algorithms construct a spanning tree by building it up edge by edge. We saw that both algorithms can also be used to construct a *maximum connector*, a concept used in *Graphs 2* in connection with the algorithm of Gomory and Hu for solving *multi-terminal flow problems*.

1.10 Travelling salesman problems

A travelling salesman wishes to visit a number of cities and return to the starting point, selling his wares as he goes. He wants to select the route that involves the least possible total distance. Which route should he choose, and what is its total length?

Unlike minimum connector problems, no efficient algorithm is known for the general travelling salesman problem. We therefore have the choice of using inefficient methods, or efficient methods that yield only approximate solutions, and we presented algorithms of both types. An example of the former is the branch-and-bound method that we described in *Graphs 4*. Examples of the latter include a greedy algorithm given in the *Introduction* unit and a method that yields a lower bound for the total length (but not a route), obtained by means of a greedy algorithm for the minimum connector problem in *Graphs 2*.

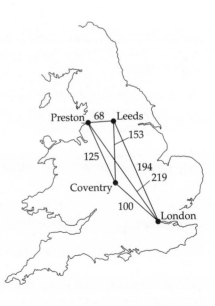

2 Combinatorics

In this section we return to one of the main themes of the course — *combinatorics*. We recall that combinatorial problems can be classified into four types, and thus that most of the problems in the course can be described under one or more of the following interrelated headings:

Existence problems   does there exist ...? is it possible to ...?

Construction problems   if ... exists, how can we construct it?

Enumeration problems   how many ... are there? can we list them all?

Optimization problems   if there are several ..., which is the best?

Let us now return to each type of problem in turn.

2.1 Existence problems

Faced with any problem, it is natural to ask *does a solution exist?* We have already mentioned various existence problems in Section 1, such as the map colouring problem and the Königsberg bridges problem.

A famous existence problem is the following puzzle.

Example 2.1: utilities problem

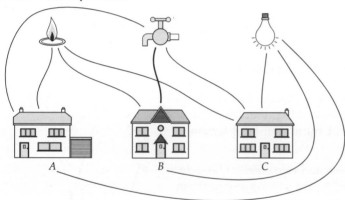

Three quarrelsome neighbours wish to connect their houses to the three 'utilities' gas, water and electricity in such a way that the various connections do not cross each other in the plane. This leads to the following existence problem:

    does there exist a way of putting in all nine connections without crossing?

It is easy to convince oneself by trial and error that the answer to the above existence problem is NO, but actually proving that a crossing must appear is more difficult.

We achieved this in *Graphs 3* by introducing the concept of a *planar graph*. We represented the situation by the bipartite graph $K_{3,3}$ in which the two sets correspond respectively to the neighbours and the utilities, and then proved that $K_{3,3}$ is non-planar. ■

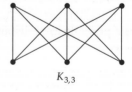

$K_{3,3}$

Sometimes it is easier to prove that something does not exist than to prove that it does. Our next example, involving block designs, is an instance of this.

Example 2.2: balanced designs

Suppose that you are asked whether there exists a balanced block design with a given set of parameters v, b, r, k and λ. In *Design 4* we established various necessary conditions for the existence of a balanced design, but these are not sufficient, so the answer may be YES, NO or DON'T KNOW.

For example, does there exist a symmetric balanced design with parameters

$$v = b = 43, r = k = 21, \lambda = 10?$$

In this case, the answer is YES, since there is a standard construction which yields such a design.

This is Construction 1 in Section 2.3 of *Design 4*.

Does there exist a symmetric balanced design with parameters

$$v = b = 46, r = k = 10, \lambda = 2?$$

In this case we can easily answer NO, since for a symmetric balanced design in which v is even, the number $r - \lambda$ must be a perfect square, which it is not in this case.

Design 4, Theorem 2.4.

But usually the situation is much more difficult than this. We may be given a set of parameters that satisfy all the conditions that we know, and yet may not correspond to any design. An example is the set

$$v = b = 157, r = k = 13, \lambda = 1,$$

which would correspond to a projective plane of order 12. It is not currently known whether such a projective plane exists. ■

Example 2.3: orthogonal latin squares

In 1779 Euler posed the following famous problem:

> is it possible for a group of 36 officers, comprising one of each of six different ranks from each of six different regiments, to stand in a 6×6 array in such a way that each rank is represented once in each row and column and each regiment is represented once in each row and column?

This is equivalent to asking whether there exists a pair of orthogonal latin squares of side 6; the ranks are the letters of one square and the regiments are the letters of the other.

Euler could find no solution to this problem and postulated that there was none. It was not until 1900 that G. Tarry proved, after an exhaustive search, that there is no such pair of orthogonal latin squares of side 6.

In 1934 Fisher and Yates gave a much shorter proof.

For many years it was believed to be impossible to construct a pair of orthogonal latin squares of side $n = 2m$, when m is odd. Euler himself postulated this in 1782. The first two cases are $n = 2$ ($m = 1$) and $n = 6$ ($m = 3$). It is easy to show that there can be no pair of orthogonal latin squares of side 2, and we have just mentioned that there is no pair of side 6, and so the next case, $n = 10$, became a test case for the conjecture. For many years no one found a pair of orthogonal latin squares of side 10 and every new general method of constructing orthogonal latin squares failed to deal with the case $n = 2m$, when m is odd. Thus the belief in the impossibility of such a construction became widespread.

In 1958 R. C. Bose and S. S. Shrikhande produced a pair of orthogonal latin squares of side 22 ($m = 11$). In the following year E. Parker constructed a pair of orthogonal latin squares of side 10. Finally, in 1960 the conjecture was well and truly buried when Bose, Shrikhande and Parker proved that there exist orthogonal latin squares for *all* such values of n except $n = 2$ and $n = 6$. ■

2.2 Construction problems

Once we know that a solution to a problem exists, we should like to find a way of constructing it.

As we saw above, we can often show that an existence problem can be solved by *constructing* a solution, but this is not always the case. In some problems we know that solutions exist because there are theoretical reasons for this, but these reasons may not give us any clue as to how a specific solution may be constructed. In other problems, the only way to determine whether a solution exists is actually to construct it.

In this course we solved some problems by describing a construction for their solution. For example, in *Design 3* we showed how the problem of constructing a code with high error-correction capability can be solved by combining two codes into a larger one with greater error-correcting ability, and we described how such a code was constructed for use with the Mariner 9 space probe. Similarly, in *Design 4* we considered problems involving the construction of block designs with particular properties, and we gave constructions for cyclic designs, balanced designs, resolvable designs and latin square designs.

We gave examples of the following methods of construction.

Building up a solution step by step

Examples of this type included the following:

- the construction of a minimum connector edge by edge;
- the construction of a maximum tree edge by edge, in the algorithm of Gomory and Hu;
- the construction of a maximum flow by identifying flow-augmenting paths;
- the construction of a maximum matching by identifying alternating paths;
- the construction of an optimum assignment, using the Hungarian algorithm;
- the construction of an activity network;
- the construction of a critical path in an activity network;
- the construction of a schedule for a given number of workers.

Note that many of these constructions use a **labelling procedure** in which the *vertices* are systematically labelled to indicate the next step in the construction.

Constructing new items from old

Examples of this type included the following:

- forming the *dual* of a tiling, polyhedron, linear code, block design, planar graph or electrical network;
- forming the *complement* of a graph or block design;
- *extending* a code by adding an overall parity check;
- putting two codes together using the [**a** | **a** + **b**] construction to obtain a code with better error-correcting properties;
- putting two block designs together to obtain larger balanced designs or resolvable designs;
- constructing a code from a block design, or a block design from a code.

Constructions that change one problem into another

Examples of this type included the following:

- converting a network with upper and lower capacities into a basic network;
- adding dummy vertices to the bipartite graph representing an assignment problem in which the number of vertices in X is not the same as the number of vertices in Y;
- converting a transhipment problem into a transportation problem.

2.3 Enumeration problems

Once we know that a particular problem has a solution, and we can construct such solutions, the next questions are

> how many solutions are there?

> what are they?

We distinguished between these two types of problem. A *counting* problem is one in which we wish to know *how many* objects of a certain kind there are; a *listing* problem is one in which we wish to produce a *list* of all these objects. These problems are very different. For example, there is an enormous difference between asking how many labelled trees there are with 8 vertices — the answer is $8^6 = 262144$, by Cayley's theorem — and asking for a list of all of them. The number of such graphs is simply too large.

This is an example of the combinatorial explosion.

Table 1 gives the results of various counting problems for graphs and digraphs.

Table 1 Numbers of graphs and digraphs of particular types

number of vertices	1	2	3	4	5	6	7	8
labelled graphs	1	2	8	64	1024	32768	2097152	268435456
unlabelled graphs	1	2	4	11	34	156	1044	12346
unlabelled connected graphs	1	1	2	6	21	112	853	11117
unlabelled regular graphs	1	2	2	4	3	8	6	20
unlabelled Eulerian graphs	1	0	1	1	4	8	37	184
unlabelled Hamiltonian graphs	1	0	1	3	8	48	383	6020
labelled trees	1	1	3	16	125	1296	16807	262144
unlabelled trees	1	1	1	2	3	6	11	23
labelled digraphs	1	4	64	4096	2^{20}	2^{30}	2^{42}	2^{56}
unlabelled digraphs	1	3	16	218	9608	1540944	$\sim 9 \times 10^9$	$\sim 2 \times 10^{12}$

In some cases, the problems of counting and listing are closely related. For example, the easiest way of counting something may be to construct a list of all possibilities and then to count how many there are. In many instances the listing problem is much harder to solve than the corresponding counting problem.

However, there are enumeration problems whose solution is unknown. An example is the enumeration of polyominoes, mentioned in *Design 1*. It is easy to list all the polyominoes with 4 squares — there are five of them — and it is not difficult to build up polyominoes with a few more squares. However, it is not known how many polyominoes there are with, say, 50 squares.

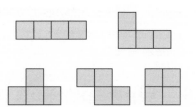

Another unsolved enumeration problem is that of counting latin squares. The number of different latin squares of side n is known only for $n \leq 9$, and grows very rapidly. For example, there are 148520 different latin squares of side 5, and for general n the number is known to be not less than $(n!)^{2n} / n^{n^2}$.

In Tables 2 and 3 we list some enumeration problems related to topics introduced in the course. Table 2 lists some solved enumeration problems, together with authors of the published solutions, and Table 3 lists some unsolved problems.

Table 2 Solved enumeration problems

graphs	Pólya, 1935
simple graphs	Pólya, 1935
cubic graphs (regular of degree 3)	R.W. Robinson, 1977
connected graphs	Riddel and Uhlenbeck, 1953 Harary, 1955
bipartite graphs	Harary and Prins, 1963
signed graphs	Harary, 1953 Harary and Palmer, 1967
Eulerian graphs	R.W. Robinson, 1969
trees	Pólya, 1937
labelled trees	Cayley, 1889
rooted trees	Pólya, 1937
forests	Harary and Palmer, 1969
digraphs	Harary, 1955
simple digraphs	Harary, 1955
connected digraphs	Harary, 1955
tournaments	Davis, 1954
Eulerian trails in a given digraph	de Bruijn and Ehrenfest, 1951 Smith and Tutte, 1941
oriented graphs	Harary, 1957

Table 3 Unsolved enumeration problems

Eulerian trails in a given graph

Hamiltonian cycles in a given graph

Hamiltonian graphs

strongly connected digraphs

graphs with given edge connectivity λ

graphs with given vertex connectivity κ

n-ominoes

planar graphs

k-colourable graphs

planar k-colourable graphs

latin squares

2.4   Optimization problems

For many combinatorial problems it is not enough to know that a given problem has a solution. It may not even be enough to be able to construct a solution using an efficient algorithm, or to list all the possible solutions. In many cases we need to find the 'best' solution, and part of the problem may be in deciding what is meant by the word 'best'. For some optimization problems, such as the minimum connector problem, there are efficient algorithms: for others, such as the travelling salesman problem or the bin-packing problem, we may have to use heuristic algorithms and we are then faced with the problem of determining whether the solution found is indeed optimal. In Section 4 we remind you of several of the optimization problems studied in this course, and of the algorithms we used for solving them.

3 Representing situations diagrammatically

3.1 Graph representations

Throughout the course we have represented situations by graphs, digraphs and networks, and we have seen that an appropriate diagrammatic representation is often a key step in finding a solution.

Graphs

In representing situations by graphs, we have seen many instances of particular types of graph.

Trees

A *tree* is the simplest type of connected graph, so in testing any conjecture about graphs, it is useful to begin by testing it for trees.

We met trees in all three subject areas of the course:

- finding minimum connectors and maximum connectors (*Graphs 2*);
- counting alkanes (*Graphs 2*);
- representing images on a screen (*Graphs 4*);
- breadth-first and depth-first searches (*Graphs 4*);
- finding fundamental cycles and fundamental cutsets for physical networks (*Networks 4*);
- determining whether a braced rectangular framework is minimally braced (*Design 2*).

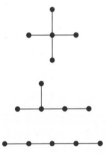

A particularly important concept is that of a *spanning tree*. The number of spanning trees in a given graph may be very large. For example, the complete graph K_5 has 125 spanning trees: 5 spanning trees isomorphic to the first tree in the margin, 60 spanning trees isomorphic to the second tree, and 60 spanning trees isomorphic to the third tree.

Bipartite graphs

In many situations, the most appropriate form of graph representation is a *bipartite graph*.

Bipartite graphs occurred in the following contexts:

- graphs in which every cycle has even length (*Graphs 1*);
- graphs with chromatic number 2 (*Graphs 3*);
- representations of braced rectangular frameworks (*Design 2*);
- graphs associated with block designs (*Design 4*);
- representations of matching, assignment, and transportation problems (*Networks 3*).

Direct graphs and interchange graphs

In *Design 2* we saw two ways in which a kinematic system can be represented by a graph. If the system has only binary *links*, then we can use the *direct* graph representation, which 'looks like' the system:

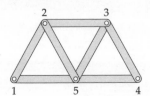 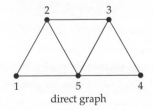

direct graph

17

If the system has only binary *joints*, then we can use the *interchange* graph representation:

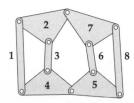
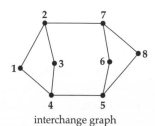

interchange graph

If the system has multiple *joints*, then we can split the joint into a number of binary joints and thereby obtain a graph representation. If there are multiple *links*, then this is not possible, but we can generalize the concept of a graph and represent the system by a *hypergraph*.

Hypergraphs are discussed in Section 3.2.

Planar graphs

We saw that a planar graph can be characterized completely in terms of the graphs K_5 and $K_{3,3}$:

> a graph is planar if and only if it contains no subdivision of K_5 or of $K_{3,3}$.

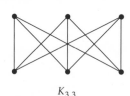

However, this does not lead to any useful general method for determining whether a given graph is planar.

An important concept defined for planar graphs is that of a *dual* graph. The relationships between various ideas associated with duals is illustrated by the following example.

Example 3.1

Consider the following graph G and its incidence matrix:

We obtained this matrix in *Graphs 1*, page 56.

$$\begin{bmatrix} 1 & 0 & 0 & 1 & 0 & 0 \\ 1 & 1 & 0 & 0 & 1 & 1 \\ 0 & 1 & 1 & 0 & 0 & 0 \\ 0 & 0 & 1 & 1 & 1 & 1 \end{bmatrix}$$

The cycles and cutsets of G, written in terms of the edges, are as follows:

cycles	cutsets
1234	14
145	23
146	3456
235	1256
236	1356
56	2456

Now let us take the incidence matrix of G and discard the last row, which is the sum (modulo 2) of the first three rows. We can form two codes — the code C which has the above matrix as *generator* matrix, and its dual C^* which has the above matrix as *parity check* matrix:

18

	code C							code C*						
bits	1	2	3	4	5	6		1	2	3	4	5	6	
no rows	0	0	0	0	0	0		0	0	0	0	0	0	
r_1	1	0	0	1	0	0	14	0	0	0	0	1	1	56
r_2	1	1	0	0	1	1	1256	0	1	1	0	1	0	235
r_3	0	1	1	0	0	0	23	1	0	0	1	1	0	145
$r_1 + r_2$	0	1	0	1	1	1	2456	0	1	1	0	0	1	236
$r_1 + r_3$	1	1	1	1	0	0	1234	1	0	0	1	0	1	146
$r_2 + r_3$	1	0	1	0	1	1	1356	1	1	1	1	0	0	1234
$r_1 + r_2 + r_3$	0	0	1	1	1	1	3456	1	1	1	1	1	1	

In the code C, the bit numbers in the non-zero codewords correspond to the edges of the *cutsets*; in the dual code C^* the bit numbers in the non-constant codewords (those other than 000000 and 111111) correspond to the edges of the *cycles*.

We can similarly associate a code and a dual code with any graph G. When G is the cycle graph C_n, the code C is the even-weight code of length n, and the dual code is the repetition code $R(n)$. ∎

Note that, in C, we also obtain the word 1234 obtained from combining the two cutsets 14 and 23.

3.2 Hypergraph representations

In our earlier discussion of kinematic systems, we remarked that it is not possible to represent a general kinematic system with multiple links by means of a graph. We can get round this problem by considering a generalization of a graph in which each edge can have an arbitrary number of vertices associated with it, instead of just two. Such an object is called a *hypergraph*.

> ### Definition
>
> A **hypergraph** H consists of a set $V(H)$ of elements called **vertices** and a set $E(H)$ of elements called **hyperedges**. Each hyperedge is a subset of V containing one or more vertices, and is said to **join** them.

Any hypergraph has an associated *incidence matrix*, which is defined as follows:

> ### Definition
>
> The **incidence matrix** of a hypergraph with n vertices and m hyperedges is the $n \times m$ matrix with n rows labelled by the vertices and m columns labelled by the hyperedges, in which the entry in row v and column e is
>
> 1,   if vertex v lies in hyperedge e
>
> 0,   if vertex v does not lie in hyperedge e.

When drawing hypergraphs, we usually draw a loop for each hyperedge with one vertex, a graph-type edge for each hyperedge with two vertices, and a closed plane-segment containing the corresponding vertices for each hyperedge with more than two vertices.

Example 3.2

The following diagram shows a hypergraph and its incidence matrix:

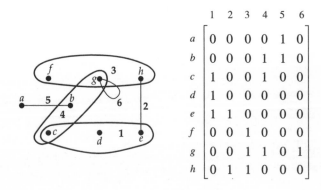

$$
\begin{array}{c}
 & 1\ \ 2\ \ 3\ \ 4\ \ 5\ \ 6 \\
\begin{array}{c}
a \\ b \\ c \\ d \\ e \\ f \\ g \\ h
\end{array}
&
\left[
\begin{array}{cccccc}
0 & 0 & 0 & 0 & 1 & 0 \\
0 & 0 & 0 & 1 & 1 & 0 \\
1 & 0 & 0 & 1 & 0 & 0 \\
1 & 0 & 0 & 0 & 0 & 0 \\
1 & 1 & 0 & 0 & 0 & 0 \\
0 & 0 & 1 & 0 & 0 & 0 \\
0 & 0 & 1 & 1 & 0 & 1 \\
0 & 1 & 1 & 0 & 0 & 0
\end{array}
\right]
\end{array}
$$

The hypergraph shown has eight vertices $\{a, b, c, d, e, f, g, h\}$ and six hyperedges $\{1, 2, 3, 4, 5, 6\}$. Hyperedge 1 joins the vertices c, d and e, hyperedge 2 joins the vertices e and h, hyperedge 3 joins the vertices f, g and h, hyperedge 4 joins the vertices b, c and g, hyperedge 5 joins the vertices a and b, and hyperedge 6 contains only the vertex g. For convenience, we denote a hyperedge by specifying its vertices: for example, hyperedge 1 is denoted by cde and hyperedge 6 is denoted by g. ∎

Most of the definitions given in this course for graphs can be generalized to hypergraphs. For example, a hypergraph is **regular of degree** k if each vertex appears in exactly k hyperedges. We also say that a hypergraph is **r-uniform** if each hyperedge consists of exactly r vertices; for example, any graph without loops is a 2-uniform hypergraph.

There are a number of situations in this course that can be thought of as hypergraphs. We describe three of these.

Example 3.3: the Fano plane

In *Design 1* and *Design 4* you met the Fano plane, or 7-point projective plane. This diagram has seven points and seven lines, where each point is incident with exactly three lines and each line is incident with exactly three points.

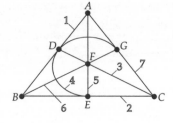

We can think of this diagram as a 3-uniform hypergraph with seven vertices A, B, C, D, E, F, G and seven hyperedges corresponding to the lines — ABD, BCE, CDF, DEG, EFA, FGB and GAC. ∎

Recall from *Design 4* that the Fano plane is a symmetric balanced block design with parameters $v = b = 7$, $r = k = 3$, $\lambda = 1$. We can associate a uniform hypergraph with any block design in a similar way.

Example 3.4: block designs

Consider the following block design with parameters $v = 9$, $b = 6$, $r = 2$, $k = 3$:

1	2	3	4	5	6
A	C	G	E	D	I
G	D	B	F	H	B
E	H	A	I	C	F

We can consider this design as a hypergraph with nine vertices $A - I$ (the varieties) and six hyperedges 1–6 (the blocks). Each hyperedge has three vertices and so the hypergraph is a 3-uniform hypergraph. Since each vertex appears in just two hyperedges, the hypergraph is regular of degree 2. ∎

More generally, given any block design with parameters v, b, r and k, we obtain a hypergraph with v vertices and b hyperedges; this hypergraph is a k-uniform hypergraph which is regular of degree r.

Note that a graph is a hypergraph in which each edge joins exactly one or two vertices.

Example 3.5: kinematic systems

Consider the following kinematic system consisting of eight links and ten joints. We can think of this system as a hypergraph with ten vertices {1, 2, ... , 10} and eight hyperedges {**1**, **2**, **3**, **4**, **5**, **6**, **7**, **8**}; for example, hyperedge **1** joins vertices 1 and 6, hyperedge **2** joins vertices 1, 2 and 7, and so on.

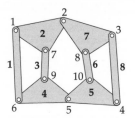 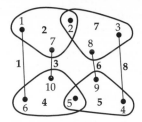

Notice that we have a representation which 'looks like' the system.

Any kinematic system can be thought of as a hypergraph in this way. There is no restriction on the types of links and joints present. ∎

Notice how the incidence matrix of a hypergraph generalizes the incidence matrix of both a graph (*Graphs 1*) and a block design (*Design 4*). Thus we see the unifying power of hypergraphs.

Dual hypergraphs

Suppose that we have a hypergraph H, with set of vertices $V(H)$ and set of hyperedges $E(H)$. We can construct another hypergraph H^* in which $E(H)$ is taken as the new vertex set $V(H^*)$. To each vertex there corresponds a set of hyperedges in $E(H)$ that each contain the given vertex. These sets of edges are considered as the new edge set $E(H^*)$ of the new hypergraph H^*. The new hypergraph H^* is called the **dual hypergraph** of H.

Example 3.2 continued

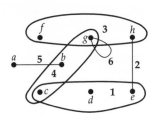 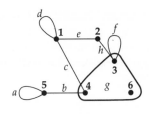

hypergraph H	dual hypergraph H^*
$V(H) = \{a, b, c, d, e, f, g, h\}$	$V(H^*) = \{1, 2, 3, 4, 5, 6\}$
$E(H) = \{1, 2, 3, 4, 5, 6\}$	$E(H^*) = \{a, b, c, d, e, f, g, h\}$
hyperedge 1 = $\{c, d, e\}$	hyperedge $a = \{5\}$
hyperedge 2 = $\{e, h\}$	hyperedge $b = \{4, 5\}$
hyperedge 3 = $\{f, g, h\}$	hyperedge $c = \{1, 4\}$
hyperedge 4 = $\{b, c, g\}$	hyperedge $d = \{1\}$
hyperedge 5 = $\{a, b\}$	hyperedge $e = \{1, 2\}$
hyperedge 6 = $\{g\}$	hyperedge $f = \{3\}$
	hyperedge $g = \{3, 4, 6\}$
	hyperedge $h = \{2, 3\}$

For example, in H, vertex g belongs to hyperedges 3, 4 and 6, and so in H^*, hyperedge g joins vertices 3, 4 and 6.

In this example, the hypergraph represents the structure of a relation in terms of the subsets of *elements*, whilst its dual represents the structure in terms of subsets of *relations*. We have 'dual' ways of looking at the same structure. Notice that the incidence matrix of the dual hypergraph H^* is the transpose of that of H:

	1	2	3	4	5	6
a	0	0	0	0	1	0
b	0	0	0	1	1	0
c	1	0	0	1	0	0
d	1	0	0	0	0	0
e	1	1	0	0	0	0
f	0	0	1	0	0	0
g	0	0	1	1	0	1
h	0	1	1	0	0	0

incidence matrix of H

	a	b	c	d	e	f	g	h
1	0	0	1	1	1	0	0	0
2	0	0	0	0	1	0	0	1
3	0	0	0	0	0	1	1	1
4	0	1	1	0	0	0	1	0
5	1	1	0	0	0	0	0	0
6	0	0	0	0	0	0	1	0

incidence matrix of H^*

Example 3.5 continued

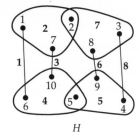

H

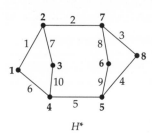

H^*

In this example, the kinematic structure has eight links and ten joints. The hypergraph H shows a representation with the joints as vertices, and the dual hypergraph H^* shows a representation with the links as vertices. This dual hypergraph is the usual interchange graph representation of kinematic structure.

Thus, the two ways of representing a kinematic structure, corresponding to the hypergraph and its dual, express the structure differently. In the hypergraph, we take the joints as elements and the links as relations between the joints. In the dual hypergraph, we consider the links as elements and the joints as relations between the links. ∎

4 Algorithms

In this section we return to the subject of NP-completeness, introduced in the *Introduction* unit, and consider the nature and efficiency of some of the algorithms presented in the course.

4.1 NP-completeness

NP-problems

We remarked earlier that nobody has been able to find a polynomial-time algorithm for the travelling salesman problem. Suppose that, instead of the usual travelling salesman problem:

> find a sequence of cities that form a Hamiltonian cycle of minimum length,

we consider the related problem:

> is there a Hamiltonian cycle of total length less than k?

where k is some number. This is called the corresponding **decision problem**.

Suppose that we have a particular instance of this problem, and that we are *given* a cycle whose total length is less than k. If we wish to *check* that the given cycle really does have total length less than k, then this is quite straightforward: the checking can certainly be done in polynomial time. Any problem like this whose solution *when given* can be *checked* in polynomial time (even if it took exponential time to find that solution originally) is called a **non-deterministic polynomial-time problem**, abbreviated to **NP-problem**. The class of all such problems is denoted by **NP**.

In particular, any problem that can be solved in polynomial time is an NP-problem, because we can certainly *check* the given solution in polynomial time if it took us only polynomial time to find it in the first place! Problems whose solution can be found in polynomial time using an algorithm form the class of **polynomial-time problems**, denoted by **P**.

To compare the performance of algorithms for problems in the class NP with algorithms for problems in P in a more formal manner, logicians have introduced the concept of a *non-deterministic computer*. This model of computation is deliberately unrealistic and corresponds to no existing physical computing device. An ordinary computer is a *deterministic* machine, in which the state at a particular time is determined in a predictable manner by the state and input to the machine at a previous time. A non-deterministic computer is a hypothetical device with the remarkable ability to 'guess' the answer to a problem.

Consider the effort involved in *originating* the solution to a problem as compared to *checking* someone else's solution.

For the decision-problem form of the travelling salesman problem, the 'guess' takes the form of a sequence of cities. The computer can then verify that the 'guess' is a solution — that is, that the sequence forms a cycle with a total length less than k. This *checking stage* can be carried out in polynomial time by a deterministic process. Thus the non-deterministic computer operates in two stages:

> a 'guessing' stage;
>
> a checking stage, in which the computer verifies that the 'guess' is in fact a solution.

The non-deterministic computer always 'guesses' correctly. The reason for having a checking stage in the non-deterministic computer is so that the performance of an algorithm for a non-deterministic computer can be compared with the performance of an algorithm for an ordinary deterministic machine.

It is assumed that the 'guessing' stage takes no appreciable time, so in this case, since the checking stage can be carried out in polynomial time, the non-deterministic computer can answer the decision form of the travelling salesman problem in polynomial time. Thus an NP-problem (non-deterministic polynomial-time problem) is one that can be solved in polynomial time on a non-deterministic computer.

We can use the non-deterministic computer to solve a decision problem — if the answer is YES, the computer produces a 'guess' and verifies it in polynomial time; if the answer is NO, the computer either produces this answer or does not stop running. In particular, if we want to find the chromatic number of a graph G, then we can obtain the answer by asking: is $\chi(G)$ less than 20? is $\chi(G)$ between 11 and 20? and so on.

Let us take another example of a problem that cannot be solved in polynomial time — the graph isomorphism decision problem:

> given two graphs G and H, are they isomorphic?

To date, the best known algorithm for solving this problem is an exponential-time algorithm. But suppose that, for a particular instance of this problem, an isomorphism between G and H *is given*. Then it takes only polynomial time to verify that this one-to-one correspondence really is an isomorphism. A non-deterministic computer can therefore solve the graph isomorphism decision problem by producing a one-to-one correspondence in the 'guessing' stage, and then verifying that this is an isomorphism in the checking stage. Hence this problem is an NP-problem.

Some important results

We now state and discuss three important results concerning the classes of problems.

The class P is contained in NP.

Each decision problem in P is also in NP, since if a problem is solvable in polynomial time on a deterministic computer, then we can solve it using a non-deterministic computer by ignoring the guessing stage and using the deterministic algorithm instead of the checking stage. Are there any problems in NP that are not in P? Algorithms for a non-deterministic computer would seem to be much more powerful than algorithms for a deterministic computer, and so we should intuitively expect NP to contain more problems than P. However, nobody has yet been able to prove this, and it remains a conjecture, although one that is generally accepted to be true.

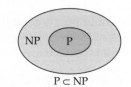

$P \subset NP$

Is P a proper subclass of NP?

A polynomial-time algorithm for a non-deterministic computer can be converted to an exponential-time algorithm for a deterministic computer.

To convert an algorithm for a non-deterministic computer to one for a deterministic machine, we must replace the guessing stage by a deterministic process. The only obvious way of doing this is to try all possible guesses. Unfortunately, the number of possible guesses is usually an exponential function of the problem size. It can be shown that a problem of size n in NP can be solved by an algorithm for a deterministic computer which has time-complexity $2^{p(n)}$, where $p(n)$ is a polynomial function. It seems likely, therefore, that there are problems in NP for which the only possible algorithms for a deterministic machine have exponential time complexity.

A decision problem is no harder than the corresponding optimization problem.

We can associate a decision problem with any optimization problem. For example, if an optimization problem requires a solution which has minimum cost or minimum length, we can associate with it a decision problem which asks whether there is a solution whose cost or length is not more than a given bound k. Decision problems can be associated in a similar way with maximization problems by replacing 'not more than' by 'not less than'. Provided that the cost or length of a solution is easy to evaluate, a decision problem can be no harder than the corresponding optimization problem. For example, if we have solved an instance of the travelling salesman problem, all we have to do to answer the corresponding decision problem is to compare the length of a minimum cycle with the bound k in the decision problem. So, although the theory of NP-complete problems applies to decision problems, we can extend many of the results about the difficulty of a problem to the corresponding optimization problems.

Polynomial time reducibility

We have seen that polynomial-time algorithms are generally considered to be efficient, and that exponential-time algorithms are generally considered to be inefficient. In comparing the difficulty of two problems, a useful technique is to try to reduce one problem to the other — that is, to find a transformation that converts any instance of one problem to an instance of the other. If such a transformation can be carried out by a polynomial-time algorithm, and if the first problem can be solved in polynomial time, then so can the second. Polynomial-time reducibility plays an important part in the theory of NP-complete problems, as we shall see shortly.

NP-complete problems

The basis of the theory of NP-completeness was provided in 1971 by Stephen Cook of the University of Toronto in a paper entitled *The complexity of theorem-proving procedures*. In this paper, he proved that one particular problem in NP, called the *satisfiability problem*, has the property that every other problem in NP can be polynomially reduced to it. The implication of this is that if the satisfiability problem can be solved in polynomial time (on a deterministic computer), then so can every other problem in NP (and so NP = P). Also, if any problem in NP is intractable, in the sense that it can be solved only in exponential time, then the satisfiability problem must also be intractable (and so NP is strictly larger than P).

Subsequently, a large number of problems (including the decision form of the travelling salesman problem) have been shown to share this property of the satisfiability problem. This class of problems is called the class of **NP-complete problems**.

It follows that if a polynomial-time algorithm can be found for *any one* of these NP-complete problems, then *every one* of them must be solvable in polynomial time; conversely, if one of them can be proved to be intractable, then they must all be intractable. The question of whether NP-complete problems are intractable is generally considered to be one of the principal unsolved problems of the theory of algorithms. However, as the number of problems shown to be NP-complete grows, and no polynomial-time algorithm is found for any of them, it becomes more and more likely that NP-complete problems are intractable.

A list of some combinatorial problems that are known to be NP-complete is given in an Appendix at the end of the unit.

4.2   Algorithms presented in the course

We now briefly discuss some of the problems and algorithms introduced in the course.

Finding Eulerian trails and Hamiltonian cycles

The Eulerian trail problem belongs to P, whereas the Hamiltonian cycle problem is NP-complete.

Eulerian problems are **Easy**; Hamiltonian problems are **Hard**.

Tiling problem

It has been proved that there is *no* algorithm which can answer all instances of the following problem: 'is it possible to tile the plane with copies of a single tile, not necessarily regular or convex?' Such a problem is said to be **undecidable**.

Maximum flow problems

The maximum flow algorithm in *Networks 1* is essentially the algorithm using flow-augmenting paths originally developed by L. R. Ford and D. R. Fulkerson in 1956. In all our examples, the capacities of the arcs were *integers*, so each flow-augmenting path enabled us to increase the value of the flow by at least 1, and this ensured that the algorithm converged to a maximum flow.

The time complexity function for this algorithm depends on the capacities of the arcs, and so we cannot give a neat expression in terms of the numbers of vertices and/or arcs of the network. Moreover, in some cases the algorithm is very slow to converge. Ford and Fulkerson constructed the following network in which four special arcs $(X_1 Y_1, X_2 Y_2, X_3 Y_3, X_4 Y_4)$ have capacities $1, c, c^2$ and c^2, where $c = (-1 + \sqrt{5})/2 = 0.618...$, and the remaining arcs have capacity $C = (3 + \sqrt{5})/2 = 2.618...$. Arcs without arrows are two-way arcs. This network has a maximum flow of value $4C$, where $C = 1 + c + c^2 + ...$ and yet, with a somewhat contrived choice of flow-augmenting paths, the algorithm produces a 'maximum' flow whose value is only C.

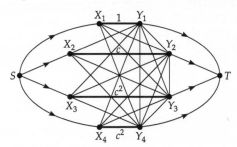

This example is rather artificial, as it involves irrational capacities, but it is nevertheless worrying, and it accelerated the search for a more satisfactory algorithm for which the complexity does not depend on the capacities.

More efficient algorithms have been designed, based on the concept of a *layered network*. This involves replacing a single maximum flow problem by a number of smaller problems; with this approach, algorithms with time complexity $O(n)$ have been obtained, where n is the number of vertices.

Shortest and longest path problems

The shortest path algorithm is efficient, with time complexity $O(n^2)$. However, the problem of finding a longest path for a general graph or network (which may contain cycles) is NP-complete.

Bin-packing

The bin-packing problem is NP-complete. However, there exist good heuristic algorithms; for example, the next-fit algorithm uses at most twice the correct number of bins, and there are many better algorithms.

Graph colouring problems

The graph vertex colouring and edge colouring problems are both NP-complete. Even though upper bounds for $\chi(G)$ and $\chi'(G)$ are known, and it is known that for simple graphs $\chi'(G)$ must be either d or $d + 1$, where d is the maximum vertex degree in G, the general problems belong to NP.

Knapsack problem

The knapsack problem is NP-complete. The branch-and-bound method of solution has worst case complexity $O(2^n)$, but usually works quite well in practice.

Travelling salesman problem

Whole books have been written on this NP-complete problem, and much research is currently under way. The problem is important because it applies not only to routing problems, but also to such problems as drilling holes in an optimal manner in printed circuit boards, in which thousands of holes may be required. In recent years Alitalia Airlines have calculated a solution for connecting 535 airports around the world.

Algorithms in the course

We conclude this section with a list of some of the algorithms presented in this course.

Minimum connector
- Kruskal's greedy algorithm   (*Introduction, Graphs 2*)
- Prim's greedy algorithm   (*Introduction, Graphs 2*)

Travelling salesman
- heuristic algorithm   (*Introduction*)
- lower bound for length of cycle   (*Graphs 2*)
- branch-and-bound method   (*Graphs 4*)

Eulerian trail in digraph   (*Networks 2*)

Hamiltonian cycles in digraph   (*Networks 2*)

Network flows
- maximum flow algorithm   (*Networks 1*)
- feasibility algorithm   (*Networks 1*)
- Gomory and Hu algorithm   (*Graphs 2*)

Shortest and longest paths
- shortest path in digraph   (*Networks 2*)
- longest path in digraph (no cycles)   (*Networks 2*)

Activity networks
- construction of network   (*Networks 2*)
- critical path construction   (*Networks 2*)
- finding latest starting times   (*Networks 2*)

Scheduling
- critical path scheduling   (*Networks 2*)

Bin packing
- next-fit packing   (*Networks 2*)
- first-fit packing   (*Networks 2*)
- first-fit decreasing packing   (*Networks 2*)

Planarity
- cycle method   (*Graphs 3*)

Colouring
- vertex colouring (greedy)   (*Graphs 3*)
- edge colouring (greedy)   (*Graphs 3*)

Matching problems
- maximum matching   (*Networks 3*)
- optimum assignment   (*Networks 3*)
- bottleneck assignment   (*Networks 3*)
- transportation problem   (*Networks 3*)

Knapsack problem
- branch-and-bound method   (*Graphs 4*)

Listing and sorting algorithms
- algorithms to search a list   (*Graphs 4*)
- bubble sort   (*Graphs 4*)
- merge sort   (*Graphs 4*)

Tree algorithms
- GROW-TREE algorithm   (*Graphs 4*)
- algorithms to search a binary tree   (*Graphs 4*)
- north neighbour algorithm   (*Graphs 4*)

5   Modelling with graphs and networks

In this course the means of representation as a model has usually concerned graphs and networks, and the manipulation of information has often been effected by means of graph or network algorithms. The nature of algorithms and their implementation on computers lends further importance to the formal structure of the models. Without these formal structures, it would be almost impossible to write algorithms. Even if algorithms were constructed, the relations of these algorithms and their conclusions to the models, and ultimately to the problems under investigation, would be extremely tenuous.

5.1   Graph models

Graphs have been 'invented' many times. As we saw in the *Introduction* unit and *Graphs 1*, the essential idea appeared in Leonhard Euler's paper of 1736 on the Königsberg bridges problem. Even though Euler did not draw a graph, the organization of the relevant features of Königsberg by such a diagram allows us to answer the problem posed.

A great stride in the development of graphs came in 1847 when Kirchhoff used graph-theoretical ideas — in particular, fundamental cycles and fundamental cutsets — to determine the voltages and currents in an electrical network.

However, even at this stage, there was no conception of a general theory of graph representations. If graphs were required, they would be re-invented for the problem at hand. This happened in the 1860s and 1870s when the structure of molecules was being examined, and a 'graphic diagram' was introduced to describe this structure. This diagram was essentially a graph as we know it today. Thus the term *graph* arose for a structural diagram.

As we saw in *Graphs 2*, the graphic notation was used by Cayley in 1875 to enumerate classes of molecular structures represented by trees. The idea that these graphs could be used as general structural descriptions in fields other than chemistry started to gain momentum. The notable English mathematicians Sylvester and Clifford even conceived that they might be applied to the description of objects in the field of mathematics itself. With hindsight, this appears to have been a wrong turning to take. Clifford and Sylvester attempted to represent algebraic structure in the theory of invariants by graphs. However, they were more at home with their mathematics of invariants, and did not really want to venture too far. Sylvester wrote:

> I feel anxious as to how it will be received as it will be thought
> by many, strained and over-fanciful. It is more a "reverie"
> than a regular mathematical paper. I have however added
> some supplementary mathematical matter which will I hope
> serve to rescue the chemical portion from absolute contempt.
> It may at worst serve to suggest to chemists and Algebraists
> that they may have something to learn from each other.

In this section on graph models, we try to indicate how we can use graphs to organize our knowledge of structural features in many situations, and how graphs allow us to put into effect a wide variety of intentions. Taking a leaf out of Sylvester's book, we venture to suggest that:

> although the following text may in part seem more a "reverie"
> than a regular mathematics or technology unit, nevertheless it
> may at worst serve to suggest to technologists and
> mathematicians that they may have something to learn from
> each other.

Properties of graph models

The models that we have developed in this course are based upon the formal structures of combinatorial mathematics, and on graph theory in particular. In the situations we investigated, we selected those features that can be represented by graphs. When this representation has been made, what do we notice? Since we have neglected many features, we have one representative structure corresponding to a whole class of objects which can be distinguished only by features that are not included in the model. Each representative structure corresponds to a class of possible objects. For instance, a model of a network corresponds to many real networks in which different commodities flow along pipes or connect elements of different sizes, shapes or materials. We say that the representation induces an *equivalence* on the objects under consideration.

What kinds of features can be represented by graphs? Broadly speaking, we can represent *structural* features. This is done in either of two ways.

First,

> the elements of the structure are represented by vertices, and
> the connections between them are represented by edges.

It is these relations that constitute the structural features. As we saw in Section 3, the course contains many examples of this kind of representation, ranging from the use of bipartite graphs for matching problems to interchange graphs for kinematic structures.

Second,

> the elements of the structure are represented by edges, and the
> relations between the elements are represented by vertices.

This representation is, in a sense, the *dual* of the first. The network problems presented in this course are often modelled in this way. The edges represent the pipes, times or roads, and the vertices represent the relations or junctions between the elements. However, in *Networks 2*, the activities in the scheduling problem were considered as elements and were represented by vertices; the edges represented the precedence relations between the activities.

Solving problems represented by graphs

We have seen how graphs are used to represent structure, but this representation alone is not generally sufficient to solve problems. We need some methods for discovering what this structure implies for the objects under investigation. There are broadly two types of method.

The first type is called the *analytic method*. For graph representations, it makes use of theorems in the theory of graphs. Two simple examples are the existence of an Eulerian cycle if all the vertices have even degree, and the existence of matchings in bipartite graphs as specified in Hall's marriage theorem. Several graph theorems are of a similar type, and tell us whether a graph has a certain property. However, many properties discovered by the analytic method do not tell us anything that is directly useful: an analytic method may solve an *existence* problem, but not the corresponding *construction* problem. For example, it is all very well to know that certain types of matching *exist*, but in practice we may want to *construct* such a matching.

The second type of method is concerned directly with showing how the property can arise in the graph structure. Such a method constructs objects with the required property and may be called a *synthetic method*. In this course we encountered synthetic methods in the form of graph algorithms — for example, in *Networks 3* we gave an algorithm for finding a maximum matching.

You may have noticed that we have avoided mentioning large areas of the course in this discussion. This is because many of the representations are not just graphs, but contain additional structure. For instance, in the representation of flow networks, there are capacities associated with the edges of the networks and certain laws which the flows obey. It is often the case that the properties of this additional structure are of most interest in applications. The graph structure provides the background framework in which the important additional structure lies. It forms the bounds and constraints in which we search for properties of the additional structure. Two examples in which this additional structure is important are as follows.

In *Graphs 2* we developed the concept of a minimum spanning tree, and we described the algorithms of Kruskal and Prim for constructing such a tree. In this case, the additional structure on the graph involves weights on the edges.

In *Graphs 3* we considered the embedding of planar graphs in the plane. This imposes the structure of the plane on the graph, and the embedded graph contains information on the cyclic order of edges around the vertices. However, the embeddings are limited by the background structure of the graph in question. If the graph is highly connected, then there are generally few embeddings in the plane. In applications of planar graphs — for instance, in the layout of a buildings or the design of a printed circuit — we are primarily interested in the embeddings of an underlying planar graph. The underlying graph provides the basic structure and some functional characteristics, but an important consideration is how these functional characteristics are realized in an actual layout.

So graphs can be used to represent structural features, but we have not reflected on the detailed content of the graph theory we have developed. The purpose of this section is to provide a context in which the various elements of graph theory can be placed. We now introduce further models representing structural features that are closely connected with graph theory and may be considered as generalizations.

We have seen how to generalize those graph models in which vertices represent the elements and edges represent relations between the elements, and we have seen how to express these structures in two equivalent ways. The generalization for those graph models in which edges represent the elements and vertices represent the relations between the elements is rather different. In such models an edge is used to represent a component with terminals corresponding to its two vertices. Thus an edge might represent a pipe or wire in a flow network.

Now suppose that the component is more complicated and is considered to have more than two terminals. This type of structure is represented by an oriented graph, introduced in *Networks 4*. The internal structures of the components are represented by trees in which the vertices represent the terminals. The important part of the representation concerns the flows on the network, the laws governing the flows, and the characteristic equations of the components. These matters are concerned with the details of additional structure on the underlying graph structure and are discussed in the next subsection.

5.2 Network models

We now look at some general properties of network models and show how they may be classified according to the types of constraint acting on the variables associated with the edges (or arcs). We indicate that variables associated with the vertices are of great importance in the construction of algorithms to solve network problems.

Properties of network models

In network analysis we use a graph or digraph to represent the underlying structure of interconnections of the elements of the model. There are two ways of doing this:

> the elements may be represented by vertices and the interconnections or relations by edges or arcs;

> the elements may be represented by edges or arcs and the interconnections or relations by vertices.

We use the first method for the assignment problem: the applicants and jobs are represented by vertices and the relations between them (possible allocations of people to jobs) are represented by edges.

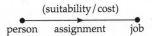

The second method is used widely in network models. An example is in the maximum-flow problem (*Networks 1*), where arcs represent the channels (roads or pipes) carrying some flow and vertices represent the connections between them.

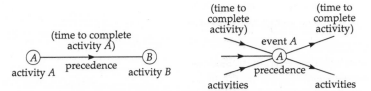

This method is also used in electrical networks where edges represent components and vertices represent the connections between them.

It is sometimes possible to represent a single problem in either way. An example is provided by the two types of activity network used to represent scheduling problems, as described in *Networks 2*.

In network problems we usually associate variables with the edges or arcs. These variables are of two distinct types. One type corresponds to the size of flow through an edge and is called a *through variable*. The other type corresponds to the difference between quantities at the vertices incident to the edge and is called an *across variable*. For instance, in electrical networks, currents are through variables and voltages are across variables.

The edge or arc variables may be subject to various types of constraint. These constraints may be of four types:

1: conservation of the sum of the through variables at each vertex — the *vertex law*;

2: conservation of the sum of the across variables around each cycle — the *cycle law*;

3: relations between the through and across variables on a given edge — the *component equations*;

4: upper and lower bounds on the flows — *capacity constraints*.

Electrical networks have severe constraints on all the variables. The through variables (currents) satisfy constraints of type 1 in the form of *Kirchhoff's current law*. The across variables satisfy constraints of type 2 in the form of

Kirchhoff's voltage law. In addition, the through and across variables (currents and voltages) are related by the *component equations*, constraints of type 3. These sets of constraints (expressed as equations relating the edge variables) enable a *unique* solution to be found to an electrical network problem for given values of the source voltages and currents. However, more general network models may not satisfy constraints of both types 1 and 2, and may also not satisfy a constraint of type 3 involving component equations. For example, the critical path scheduling algorithm (*Networks 2*) satisfies none of the above types of constraint. Thus, the number of equations expressing the constraints in a network problem may not be sufficient to give unique values for the edge variables. Usually in such cases we are required to find a solution which satisfies some kind of optimality criterion, such as minimum cost or maximum flow.

Historically, the electrical network model was the prototype for many other network models. For this reason, and also because electrical networks have such severe constraints on the variables, it is appropriate to look first at some of the concepts involved in electrical networks and then to consider the application of some of these ideas to other types of network in which the constraints are less severe.

Electrical networks

As in *Networks 4*, we consider a network for which the oriented graph has n vertices and m edges. We can express the constraints on the variables as linear equations, as follows.

Kirchhoff's current law can be written in the form

$$\mathbf{A}_{n\times m}\,\mathbf{J}_{m\times 1} = \mathbf{0}_{n\times 1},\qquad\text{(KCL)}$$

where $\mathbf{A}$ is the $n \times m$ incidence matrix of the oriented graph of the network and $\mathbf{J}$ is the $m \times 1$ column vector of currents $i_1, i_2, ..., i_m$ associated with the edges of the oriented graph.

In order to write Kirchhoff's voltage law in a similar way, we associate variables with the vertices: we define *vertex potentials* $P_1, P_2, ..., P_n$ at the vertices so that the voltage on each edge is the difference between the potentials at its end-vertices. The equations $P_i - P_j = v_k$ for all vertices can be expressed in matrix form:

$$\mathbf{A}^T_{m\times n}\mathbf{P}_{n\times 1} = \mathbf{V}_{m\times 1},\qquad\text{(KVL)}$$

where $\mathbf{A}^T$ is the transpose of the incidence matrix $\mathbf{A}$, $\mathbf{P}$ is the $n \times 1$ column vector of vertex potentials, and $\mathbf{V}$ is the $m \times 1$ column vector of voltages associated with the m edges of the graph.

In other words, if the voltages satisfy Kirchhoff's voltage law, then we can find vertex potentials such that the potential difference across each edge is equal to the difference between the vertex potentials at its end-vertices. The above matrix equation is therefore equivalent to Kirchhoff's voltage law.

Note that for a given incidence matrix $\mathbf{A}$ and vector $\mathbf{V}$, there are infinitely many vectors $\mathbf{P}$ that satisfy the KVL equation. For instance, if $\mathbf{P}$ satisfies the equation, and if $\mathbf{C}$ is a column vector with all entries the same, then $\mathbf{P} + \mathbf{C}$ also satisfies the equation. Usually the value of the potential P_j at one vertex j is fixed, so that a unique vector $\mathbf{P}$ satisfies the equation; this vertex is called the *reference vertex*.

In *Networks 4*, we showed that the above forms of Kirchhoff's current and voltage laws provide a method of deriving Tellegen's theorem, which may be stated as

$$\mathbf{V}^T_{1\times m}\mathbf{J}_{m\times 1} = \mathbf{0}_{1\times 1}.\qquad\text{(TT)}$$

We call $\mathbf{V}^T\mathbf{J}$ the *power function* of the network, and the TT-equations express the *law of conservation of energy* in the network.

Tellegen's theorem and the two Kirchhoff laws are closely related, in the sense that *any two imply the third*. In effect, *we have three equivalent statements of the electrical network problem* — namely:

$$\mathbf{A}_{n\times m}\mathbf{J}_{m\times 1} = \mathbf{0}_{n\times 1}, \quad \mathbf{A}^T_{m\times n}\mathbf{P}_{n\times 1} = \mathbf{V}_{m\times 1}, \qquad \text{(KCL and KVL)}$$

$$\mathbf{V}^T_{1\times m}\mathbf{J}_{m\times 1} = \mathbf{0}_{1\times 1}, \quad \mathbf{A}_{n\times m}\mathbf{J}_{m\times 1} = \mathbf{0}_{n\times 1}, \qquad \text{(TT and KCL)}$$

$$\mathbf{V}^T_{1\times m}\mathbf{J}_{m\times 1} = \mathbf{0}_{1\times 1}, \quad \mathbf{A}^T_{m\times n}\mathbf{P}_{n\times 1} = \mathbf{V}_{m\times 1}, \qquad \text{(TT and KVL)}$$

Any one of these three sets of equations, together with the component equations, provides enough information to solve a given electrical network problem uniquely.

Vertex variables for other types of network

We saw in the above brief presentation of the electrical network model that Kirchhoff's voltage laws can be written in terms of edge variables v_k or in terms of vertex potentials P_i. Vertex potentials are a particular type of vertex variable which are applicable for networks that satisfy Kirchhoff's voltage law or an equivalent law. For networks that do not satisfy Kirchhoff's voltage law, we cannot assign a unique potential to each vertex. Nevertheless, for such problems, vertex variables are still useful, and play an important role in algorithms constructed for their solution.

Several networks problems involve across variables that do not satisfy an equivalent form of Kirchhoff's voltage law. Examples of these are *costs* in the assignment and transportation problems of *Networks 3*, and *time* in the scheduling problems of *Networks 2*.

Note that many of the network algorithms in this course introduce vertex variables that guide us to the correct solution. This is no accident, since each such network problem has an equivalent *dual* form that involves vertex variables. Many algorithms implicitly use the equivalence of the problem and its dual, and in many cases their discovery was motivated by consideration of the dual form.

6   ...and finally

We conclude by summarizing some ideas on tackling a problem in combinatorics.

Classify the problem in as many ways as possible

- does it concern *graphs, networks* or *design*?

- if it is a graphs problem, does it involve *path-finding, planarity, colouring, decomposition, matching, domination* or *independence*?

- if it is a networks problem, does it involve *flows, path-finding, matching, assignment, transportation* or a *physical network*?

- if it is a design problem, does it involve *geometry, kinematics, block designs, codes,* or some combination of these?

- is it an *existence, construction, enumeration* or *optimization* problem?

Represent the problem diagrammatically

- can the problem be represented by a *graph, digraph, oriented graph* or *hypergraph*?

Study known results

- can you use any known results — for example, theorems, codes, block designs in catalogues?
- can you break the problem down into smaller problems, or convert it into some other problem that you know how to solve?

Test a conjecture

- test a conjecture by considering simple cases — for example, a graph or network with a small number of edges, vertices or cycles.
- test a graph conjecture by considering trees, cycles or bipartite graphs.

Determine what type of solution is required

- is there a unique solution or are there many solutions?
- if there are many, do you need to find them all, or just one?

Study existing algorithms

- is there a polynomial-time algorithm that solves the problem?
- is there a heuristic algorithm that is fast and gives the correct solution in this particular case?
- is there a heuristic algorithm that gives an acceptable approximate solution with an upper or lower bound on its accuracy?

Further reading

Of making many books there is no end; and much study is a weariness of the flesh.
(Ecclesiastes 12:12)

An elementary book covering many of the ideas discussed in this unit is:

V. K. Balakrishnan, *Introductory Discrete Mathematics*, Prentice-Hall, Inc., 1991.

Graph enumeration problems are discussed in detail in:

F. Harary and E. M. Palmer, *Graphical Enumeration*, Academic Press, 1973.

Hypergraphs are discussed in the following books:

C. Berge, *Hypergraphs*, North Holland Mathematical Library **45**, Elsevier Science Publishers B.V., 1989;

C. Berge, *Graphs and Hypergraphs*, North-Holland Publishing Co., 1973.

A full discussion of graph algorithms, including NP-completeness, may be found in:

S. Even, *Graph Algorithms*, Pitman Publishing Ltd., 1979.

H. S. Wilf, *Algorithms and Complexity*, Prentice-Hall, Inc., 1986.

T. C. Hu, *Combinatorial Algorithms*, Addison-Wesley Publishing Co., Inc., 1982.

The following important book gives a full account of all the ideas covered in Section 4, and contains an extensive list of NP-complete problems:

M. R. Garey and D. S. Johnson, *Computers and Intractability: A Guide to the Theory of NP-completeness*, W. H. Freeman and Co., 1979.

Appendix: NP-complete problems

We conclude with a list of some NP-complete graph and network problems. In the following list we denote a graph G with set of vertices V and set of edges E by $G(V, E)$, and the size of a set X by $|X|$.

TRAVELLING SALESMAN (*Introduction*)

given   a set C of cities, the distances between each pair of cities, and a positive integer k

problem   is there a tour of C with total length not exceeding k?

BIPARTITE SUBGRAPH (*Graphs 1*)

given   a graph $G(V, E)$ and a positive integer $k \leq |E|$

problem   is there a subset E' of E with $|E'| \geq k$ such that $G'(V, E')$ is bipartite?

comment   this is solvable in polynomial time if G is planar

SUBGRAPH ISOMORPHISM (*Graphs 1*)

given   two graphs $G_1(V_1, E_1)$ and $G_2(V_2, E_2)$

problem   does G_1 contain a subgraph isomorphic to G_2?

comment   this problem can be solved in polynomial time if G_1 is a forest and G_2 is a tree

HAMILTONIAN CYCLE (*Graphs 1*)

given   a graph $G(V, E)$

problem   does G contain a Hamiltonian cycle?

GENERALIZED 4-CUBES PROBLEM (*Graphs 1*)

given   a finite set C of colours, and a set Q of cubes, with $|Q| = |C|$, and each side of each cube in Q is assigned a colour in C

problem   can the cubes in Q be stacked vertically so that each colour in C appears exactly once on each of the four sides of the stack?

DEGREE-CONSTRAINED SPANNING TREE (*Graphs 2*)

given   a graph $G(V, E)$ and a fixed positive integer $k \leq |V|$

problem   is there a spanning tree of G in which no vertex has degree greater than k?

ISOMORPHIC SPANNING TREE (*Graphs 2*)

given   a graph G and a tree T

problem   does G contain a spanning tree isomorphic to T?

comment   this problem remains NP-complete even if T is a path

LONGEST PATH (*Networks 2*)

given   a graph $G(V, E)$, the length of each edge in E, a positive integer k, and two specified vertices s and t in V

problem   is there an st-path in G of length at least k?

comment   this problem remains NP-complete when each edge has length 1

BIN PACKING (*Networks 2*)

given   a finite set S of items, each of a given size, a positive integer bin capacity b and a positive integer k

problem   is there a partition of S into k disjoint subsets such that the sum of the sizes of the items in each subset does not exceed b?

PLANAR SUBGRAPH (*Graphs 3*)

given   a graph $G(V, E)$ and a positive integer $k < |E|$

problem   is there a subset E' of E with $|E'| > k$ such that $G'(V, E')$ is planar?

GRAPH k-COLOURABILITY (*Graphs 3*)

given   a graph $G(V, E)$ and a positive integer $k < |V|$

problem   is G k-colourable?

comment   this problem is solvable in polynomial time for $k = 2$

DOMINATING SET (*Graphs 3*)

given   a graph $G(V, E)$ and a positive integer $k \leq |V|$

problem   is there a dominating set of size k or less for G?

comment   the corresponding problem for trees is solvable in polynomial time

INDEPENDENT SET (*Graphs 3*)

given   a graph $G(V, E)$ and a positive integer $k < |V|$

problem   does G contain an independent set of size k or more?